This Book Belongs To

Adoption Is
LOVE

Stephanie Casaubon

AUSTIN MACAULEY PUBLISHERS™
LONDON * CAMBRIDGE * NEW YORK * SHARJAH

Copyright © Stephanie Casaubon (2020)

Ordering Information:
Quantity sales: special discounts are available on quantity purchases by corporations, associations, and others. For details, contact the publisher at the address below.

Publisher's Cataloging-in-Publication data
Casaubon, Stephanie
Adoption Is Love

ISBN 9781647500153 (Paperback)
ISBN 9781647500160 (Hardback)
ISBN 9781647500177 (ePub e-book)

Library of Congress Control Number: 2020907269

www.austinmacauley.com/us

First Published (2020)
Austin Macauley Publishers LLC
40 Wall Street, 28th Floor
New York, NY 10005
USA
mail-usa@austinmacauley.com
+1 (646) 5125767

For Willow and Eveleigh, whom I love unconditionally and beyond measure.

To all children and mothers everywhere brought together through adoption.

I wish to thank:

My darling daughters, you are the inspiration for every word on the page.
Without you, I'd be speechless.

My husband, Josh, with you, I became the mother I am today. Because of you,
I have the opportunity to create and share this work. Thank you x infinity.
It's all for love.

My mom, your confidence in me has always been the wind in my sails.

The moment I saw you, my heart skipped a beat.

After wishing upon stars, our souls got to meet.

It was love at first sight, and when I held you I knew,

that I am your mama, instantly, through and through.

I wanted you always, before you were here.

Knowing when you'd arrive was a mystery my dear.

Through adoption, our hearts found their way to each other.

I am your mama. That's me. Your mother.

Upon your head, I place kiss after kiss.

Looking deep in your eyes, I promise you this:

I choose you for all time, whether angel or wild.

I'm always your mama, you're always my child.

You have a birth family, and here's what that means:

We won't look alike, we don't share the same genes.

What makes us a family? It's the love that we keep -

alive in our hearts, when awake or asleep.

We're forever a family, there is no doubt.

Adoption blooms in the heart, for love's what it's about.

As I snuggle you close, place your hand in mine.

I'm forever your mama - our hearts now intertwined.

If things don't make sense or you're blue late at night,

talk to me, tell me when something's not right.

Tiptoe to my room, ask questions - Believe!

I am your mama, and Mama won't leave.

Now Mama's not perfect, I will make mistakes.

I'll forget your umbrella, I'll ruin pancakes.

I'll cackle too loud, I'll cuddle too tight,

and I promise to love you with all of my might.

As you grow, I know, there'll be challenges too.

I vow to be there and kiss all your boo boos.

Through the ups and downs, whether giggles or frowns,

I'm still your mama, my love knows no bounds.

Slay dragons, slide rainbows, you need to explore.

If you sail 'round the world, I'll wait by the shore.

I'll love you, protect you and guide you, that's true.

I am your mama - that's what mamas do.

When clouds hide the sun or thunderstorms reign,

you may find yourself scared, upset or in pain.

Even through tears, be brave and take leaps.

Know I'm here, I'm your mama, and that is for keeps.

Go march to the beat of your very own drum.

There is no limit to what you can become.

Keep dreaming, have courage - break free from the crowd.

I am your mama, and I'll always be proud.

As you go through this life, whether you walk or you run...

delight in the quiet, make snow angels, have fun!

Experience the world from sunrise to sunset.

No matter what, Mama loves you. Don't ever forget!

My one wish for you my starshine, my heart,

from the depths of my soul, even if we're apart:

Believe you are loved - just as you are - that's for sure!

Because adoption is LOVE, and our love will endure.

Stephanie Casaubon became a parent through adoption in 2013 and 2015. She's a writer, an advocate for adoption education, and an empowerment coach, helping women create their best life. Her favorite title, however, is mama. Stephanie resides in France with her husband and two extraordinary daughters. www.adoptionislove.com

CPSIA information can be obtained
at www.ICGtesting.com
Printed in the USA
LVHW072258151120
671787LV00013B/121

9 781647 500160